Aramazu
Finds the Hours

By Jamie Rugge-Price
Illustrated by Janine Williams

This book belongs
to

....

and
I'm learning
to tell the time.

A few days ago President Pickles had a terrible nightmare. In his dream, Princess Tempora, disguised as a sweet seller, had returned and hung him upside down in the town square as he did not have a Time Stick.

1

So the President is determined that everyone in Aramazu should learn to tell the Time, including his daughter Saffron who never knows **when** to catch the bus.

The Learn to Tell the Time store is about to open. The two clocks, Buzzer and Ormolulu are working hard; Charlie the cuckoo is practising his welcome. "Special introductory offer! Find out about the hours, o'clocks and half pasts, absolutely free!"

Bobby Buffer, the stationmaster wants to find where the o'clock is so his express trains can leave on the hour. Beryl Changegear, the bus driver, wants to know how long half an hour lasts so that she can run her bus service every half hour.

4

Six year old Evie Stickleback wants to know when it is half past eight so she can feed her puppy Brimstone each morning. Archie Moonstone wants to know all about the o'clocks and half pasts so that his friend Evie Stickleback won't be able to tell him when to do what. Sometimes she is a bit bossy.

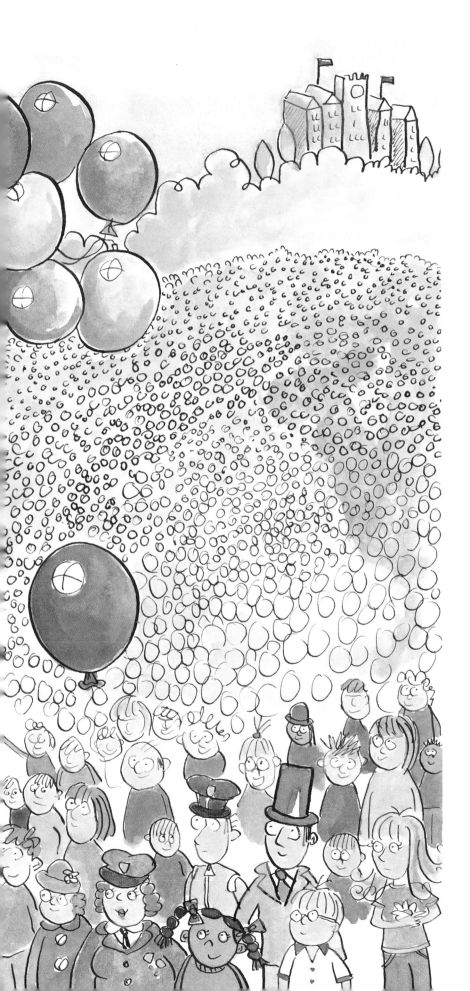

At last the world's first Learn to Tell the Time store opens its doors. So many people come they have to move onto the street. Fortunately Buzzer and Ormolulu find space on a large table.

"It is much easier to tell the Time if you know the shape of an hour" says Buzzer. "Hours are huge pieces of Time, so what shape would something so enormous be?"

"Could an hour be the shape of a mountain?" said Archie hoping Evie would not be able to think of anything bigger. Archie is right, every hour is the shape of a mountain.

"The trouble with clocks, even famous ones, is they don't show you where each hour begins and ends but let me show you something!" said Buzzer. "Pull the rope, George."

George the station clock pulls the rope, the large sheet which has been covering the clock floats down on top of him. For a moment he thinks he is back at the station, covered in steam. "The train now standing at Platform 3 is the 7.32 calling at Pidley, Podley and Puddlesworth Central...erhm... erhm... Sorreee!"

"Push the mountains onto the clock, Charlie. We call them Hour Mountains because it takes Time one whole hour to climb each one. This is the Aramazu Mountain clock, we have lots of them so make sure you get one" says Buzzer.

(**Reader note:** You will find a Mountain Clock for you to practise on at the back of this book.)

"On a clock, the short hand is the hour hand, it points to the Hour Mountain Time is on. On the Mountain Clock we have made it look like a finger. Fingers are good at pointing and they are short" says Buzzer.

(**Reader note:** Why don't you fix the finger onto your Mountain Clock?)

"Time always goes the same way round the clock, but slower than Brimstone. The flags tell Time which way to go."

Bobby Buffer the stationmaster wants his express train to leave at one o'clock. "Finding the o'clock is easy using the Mountain Clock" says Ormolulu. "It is always at the top of the hour. So when the finger points here, it's one o'clock."

"What Time does the does the train on Platform 3 leave?"
(That's right, it's five o'clock).

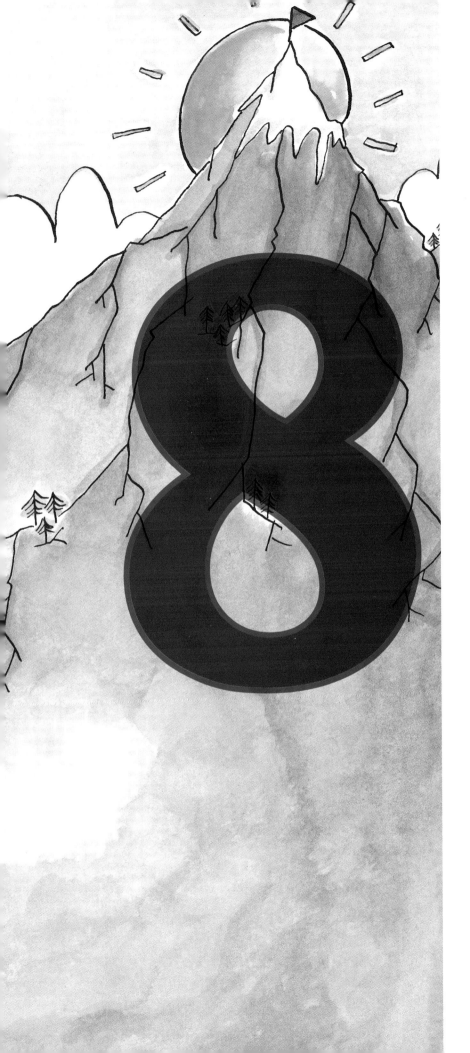

Beryl Changegear runs the Aramazu bus service and wants to know how long half an hour is. "Time takes half an hour to climb up an Hour Mountain and half an hour to come down the other side" says Buzzer.
"Half an hour is as long as your favourite TV programme each evening, or break time at school."

Evie Stickleback wants to know when it's half past eight so she can feed Brimstone. Half an hour after passing eight o'clock at the top, where will Time be?

"Time will be at the bottom of the eight hour. The half past is at the bottom of the Hour Mountain, the bit in between that Hour Mountain and the next" said Buzzer. "So when the finger points here, it's half past eight."

The last thing Archie Moonstone wants is his neighbour Evie telling him when it will be his teatime. So he is practising. Can you tell which clock is at half past three, at half past four and at half past five? Archie is pointing the finger on his Mountain Clock the same way as the short hand on the clocks. (He has his tea at half past five!)

Unknown to anybody and disguised as a friendly sweet seller Tempora, Princess of Wasted Time, has slipped back into Aramazu. She is laying out her stall of Timesticks as people gather to play Catch the Time.

(**Reader note:** Bring your practice clock if you want to play.)

Every time I shout 'Catch the Time' I shall point to a clock.

(Remember, the small hand is the hour hand)

The first person to give me six correct answers will be the winner.

"When the finger points to the top of the hour, it means 2 o'clock" says Bobby Buffer. "The Aramazu express leaves at 2 o'clock so here we go!"

"When the finger points to the bottom bit between the 3 and the 4 hour it must be half an hour past 3 o'clock, half past three. Time for a very important meeting" said President Pickles.

Suddenly the people of Aramazu are finding they understand the hours, breakfast at 8 o'clock, lunch at half past 12, tea at 5 o'clock.

Even Saffron manages to catch the 3 o'clock bus to her judo lesson.

Princess Tempora is furious! "All gone to waste just because they know about the hours. Never mind, they will soon be begging for my new 5 minute Time Sticks!"

Map of Aramazu